This book belongs to:

For Team McCallum:
Ben, Toby, Ella and Charlie.

This edition 2010

A CIP record for this book is available
from the British Library

Mantra Lingua
Global House
303 Ballards Lane
London, N12 8NP
www.mantralingua.com

Touch the arrow with the RecorderPEN to start

Start Info English Language

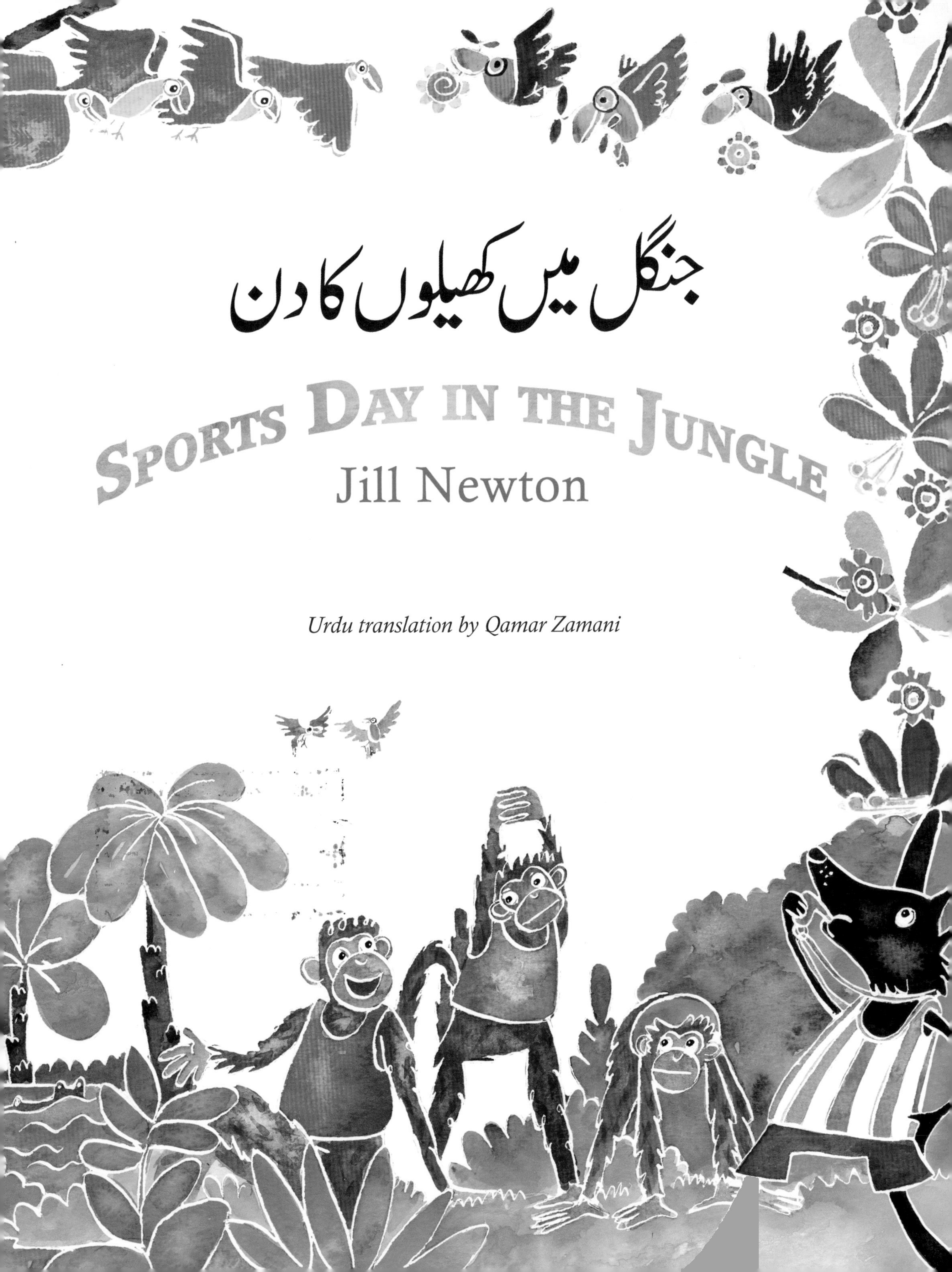

جنگل میں کھیلوں کا دن

Sports Day in the Jungle

Jill Newton

Urdu translation by Qamar Zamani

جنگل میں ہونے والے کھیلوں کا وقت قریب آ رہا تھا اور
سب جانور اُس کی مشق میں لگے ہوئے تھے۔

خیر، تقریباً سب جانور۔

It was nearly time for the jungle games, and every animal was busy practising.

Well, *almost* every animal.

کاہل ممالیہ اپنی شاخ پر بیٹھا سب کو دیکھ رہا تھا۔
وہ زیادہ حرکت نہیں کرتا تھا۔

Sloth slowly watched from his branch. He didn’t move very much.

بندر جھولتا ہوا قریب سے گزرا۔
”میری طرف دیکھو کاہل ممولیئے! مجھے پکڑ سکتے ہو تو کوشش کرلو!“

Monkey swung past.
“Look at me, Sloth! Try and catch me!”

کاہل ممالیئے نے بندر کو پیڑوں میں غائب ہوتے دیکھا۔۔۔

۔۔۔اور ایک آہ بھری۔

Sloth watched Monkey disappear
into the trees…

…and sighed.

وہ چھوٹے لنگوروں کو کودتے ہوئے، تیندوؤں کو زقند بھرتے ہوئے،
اور سرخ بالوں والے بندروں کو **جنگلی کرتب**
دکھاتے ہوئے،
دیکھتا رہا۔

He watched lemurs leap,
panthers pounce
and orangutans do *the jungle juggle.*

اور کاہل ممالیئے نے آہستہ۔۔۔

آہستہ۔۔۔

آہستہ سے اپنی آنکھیں بند کرلیں۔

And Sloth slowly...
slowly...
slowly closed his eyes.

"You can't catch me,
Sloth!"
Monkey laughed.

''تم مجھے پکڑ نہیں سکتے کاہل ممالیئے!''
بندر نے ہنس کر کہا۔

کاہل ممالیئے نے دیکھا کہ بندر شاخوں پر چکر لگاتا ہوا، جھولتا ہوا اپنی ٹولی کے انتخاب کے لئے جا رہا تھا۔۔۔

اور اُس نے آہ بھری۔

Sloth watched Monkey spin about on the branches, swinging off to the team selections…

...and sighed.

گیدڑنی نے ہر جانور کو اپنی بہترین کوشش کرتے دیکھا۔
اُس نے بندر کو منتخب کیا کیونکہ بندر ہمیشہ جیت جاتا تھا۔

Jackal looked on as every creature tried their best.
She chose Monkey first as Monkey *always* won.

کاہل ممالیئے کو کبھی نہیں چنا جاتا تھا۔
اِردگرد منڈلاتے رہنے کا کوئی مقابلہ نہیں کیا جاتا تھا۔

Nobody chose Sloth.
There was no race for
hanging about.

جانوروں کی ٹولی بہت محنت کر رہی تھی۔
سب کے سب واقعی جنگل کے کھیلوں کا مقابلہ جیتنا چاہتے تھے۔

The team
worked hard.
They all really
wanted to win
the jungle
games.

”میں ہی جیتوں گا!“ بندر نے پکار کر کہا ”کوئی مجھے نہیں پکڑ سکتا!“
تمام جانوروں نے بندر کو دیکھا۔۔۔ اور ایک آہ بھری۔

“I’m going to win!” called Monkey.
“No one can catch me!”
All the animals watched Monkey… and sighed.

ایک لمبی، بے چین رات کے بعد آخر صبح کو سورج نظر آیا۔
اور اِس کے ساتھ ہی مقابلے میں حصّہ لینے والوں کی ٹولیاں آ گئیں۔
جنگل کھیلوں کی دوڑ بھاگ سے گونج رہا تھا۔

After a long, restless night the sun finally appeared. And along with it came the competing teams.

The jungle was alive with sport.

Slowly, Sloth moved branch to
watch the tigers tumble,
the toucans tango, the elephants
humph and the
frogs hop,
skip
and jump!

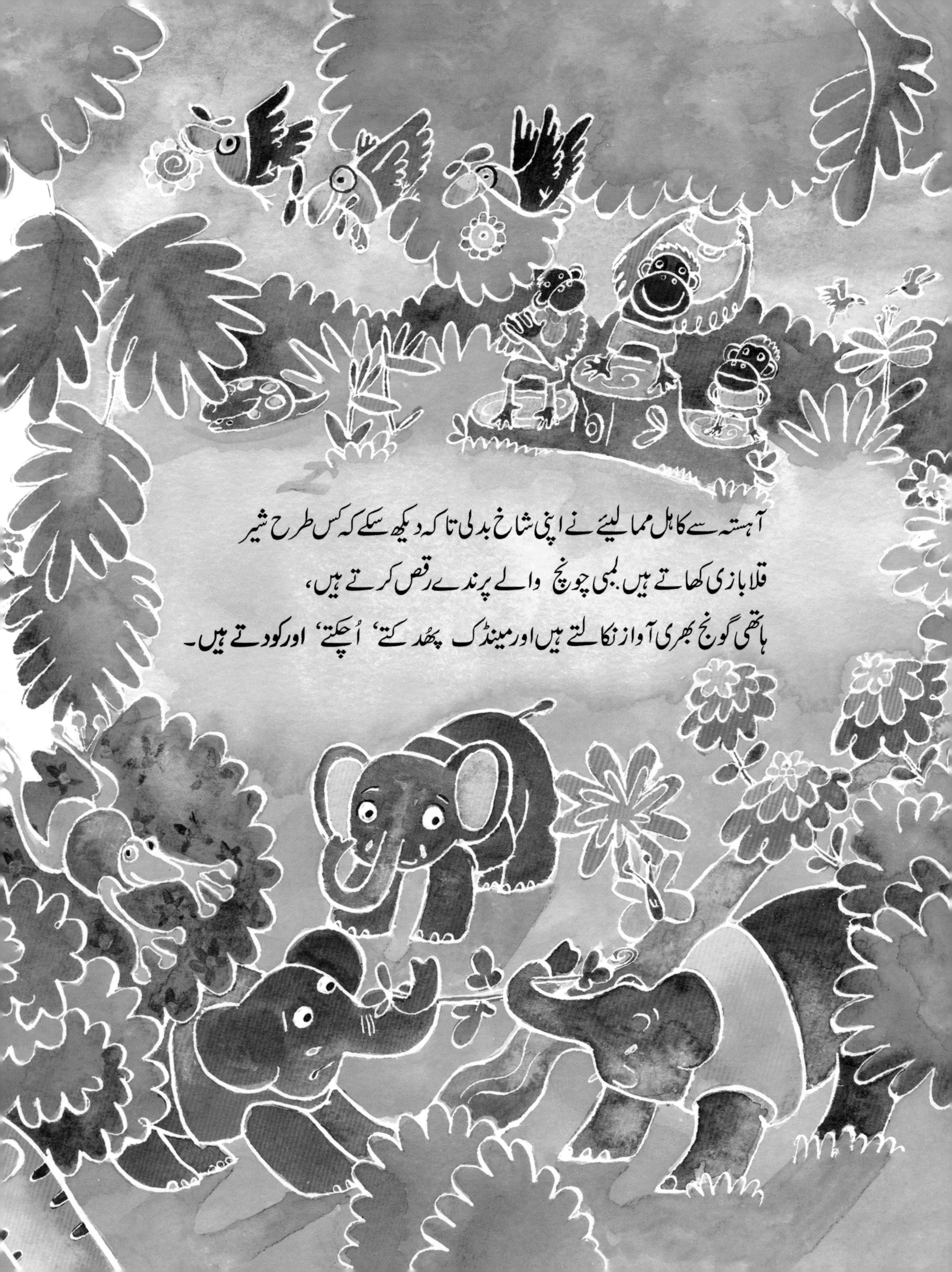

آہستہ سے کاہل ممالیئے نے اپنی شاخ بدلی تا کہ دیکھ سکے کہ کس طرح شیر
قلابازی کھاتے ہیں. لمبی چونچ والے پرندے رقص کرتے ہیں،
ہاتھی گونج بھری آواز نکالتے ہیں اور مینڈک پھُدکتے' اُچکتے' اور کودتے ہیں۔

جلد ہی اَب صرف ایک دوڑ رہ گئی تھی۔

''میرے لئے تو یہ بہت آسان ہے'' بندر نے اپنی تیاری کرتے ہوئے کہا۔

''میں تو ہوا کی طرح دوڑتا ہوں۔ **کوئی بھی، میرا مطلب ہے کوئی بھی،** مجھے پکڑ نہیں سکتا!''

Soon there was only one race left.
"It'll be a breeze," said Monkey as he got ready.
"I'm as fast as the wind. No one, *I mean no one*,
can catch me!"

بندر شاخوں پر سے گزرتا ہوا، بیلوں پر جھولتا ہوا، تیزی سے، بہت تیزی سے بڑھ رہا تھا۔
ہر ایک نے نعرہ لگایا جب فاصلہ بڑھتا گیا۔

Monkey raced from bough to branch to vine,
swinging faster and faster.
Everyone cheered as the gap got wider.

بندر کودا اور درخت کی سب سے اُونچی شاخ پکڑ لی۔۔۔

Monkey leapt and grabbed the highest branch of the tree…

The branch wasn't strong enough.

شاخ اتنی مضبوط نہیں تھی۔

کاہل ممالیہ آہستہ---

آہستہ سے اپنی شاخ پر کھڑا ہو گیا۔

Sloth slowly…
slowly...
stood up on his branch.

اُس نے اپنے لمبے بازو پھیلائے،

تب--- **ایک زبردست سنسناہٹ!**

He stretched his long arms,
then...

سب نے خوش ہو کر داد دی جب کاہل ممالیئے نے آخر کار بند کو پکڑ لیا!

Everyone cheered as
Sloth *finally* caught
Monkey!

JUNGLE FACTS

Sloths are surprisingly good at swimming.

Lemurs use their big tails to signal to each other.

Panthers are really good at climbing trees.

When a male and female toucan like each other, they use their beaks to throw fruit to each other.

Elephants make lots of interesting noises. They grunt, purr, bellow, whistle and trumpet.

Monkeys live in groups called troops.

A tiger's roar can be heard more than a mile away.

If people don't stop chopping down the jungle, very soon there won't be any jungle left.